Counting to 100

► **Fill in the missing numbers.**

1	2								10
11	12	13							20
21	22							29	
31		33							40
41								49	
	52								60
61							68		
71									80
		83						89	
91									100

► **How many? Write the number.**

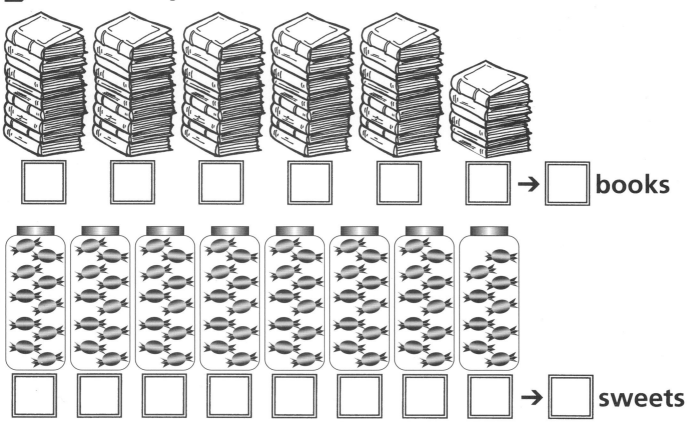

☐ ☐ ☐ ☐ ☐ ☐ → ☐ books

☐ ☐ ☐ ☐ ☐ ☐ ☐ ☐ → ☐ sweets

3

Continue the numbers.

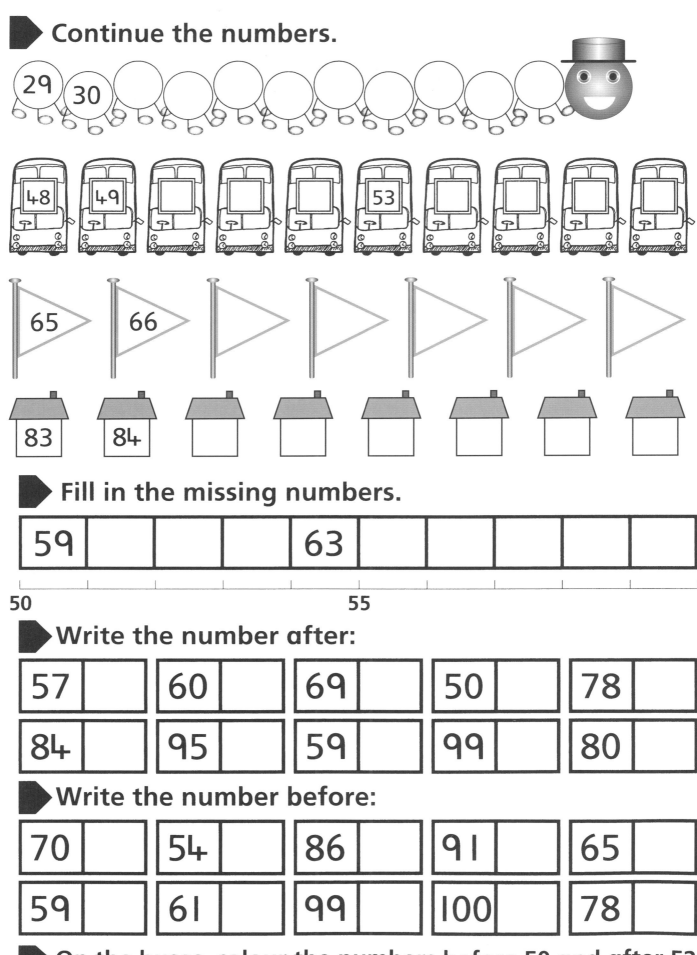

29 30

48 49 53

65 66

83 84

Fill in the missing numbers.

| 59 | | | | 63 | | | | | |

50   55

Write the number after:

| 57 | | 60 | | 69 | | 50 | | 78 | |
| 84 | | 95 | | 59 | | 99 | | 80 | |

Write the number before:

| | 70 | | 54 | | 86 | | 91 | | 65 |
| | 59 | | 61 | | 99 | | 100 | | 78 |

On the buses, colour the numbers before 50 and after 52.
On the flags, colour the numbers before 67 and after 70.

4

Tens and units

▶ **Write how many tens and units.**

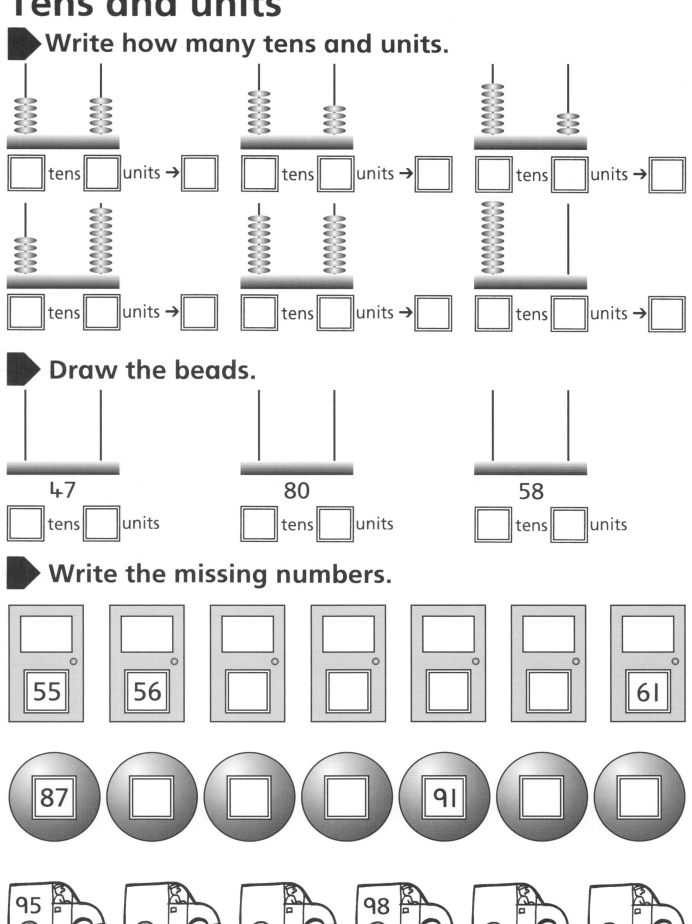

☐ tens ☐ units → ☐   ☐ tens ☐ units → ☐   ☐ tens ☐ units → ☐

☐ tens ☐ units → ☐   ☐ tens ☐ units → ☐   ☐ tens ☐ units → ☐

▶ **Draw the beads.**

47   80   58

☐ tens ☐ units   ☐ tens ☐ units   ☐ tens ☐ units

▶ **Write the missing numbers.**

| 55 | 56 | | | | | 61 |

| 87 | | | | 91 | | |

95   98

Tens and units

▶ **Use rods to work out the answers.**

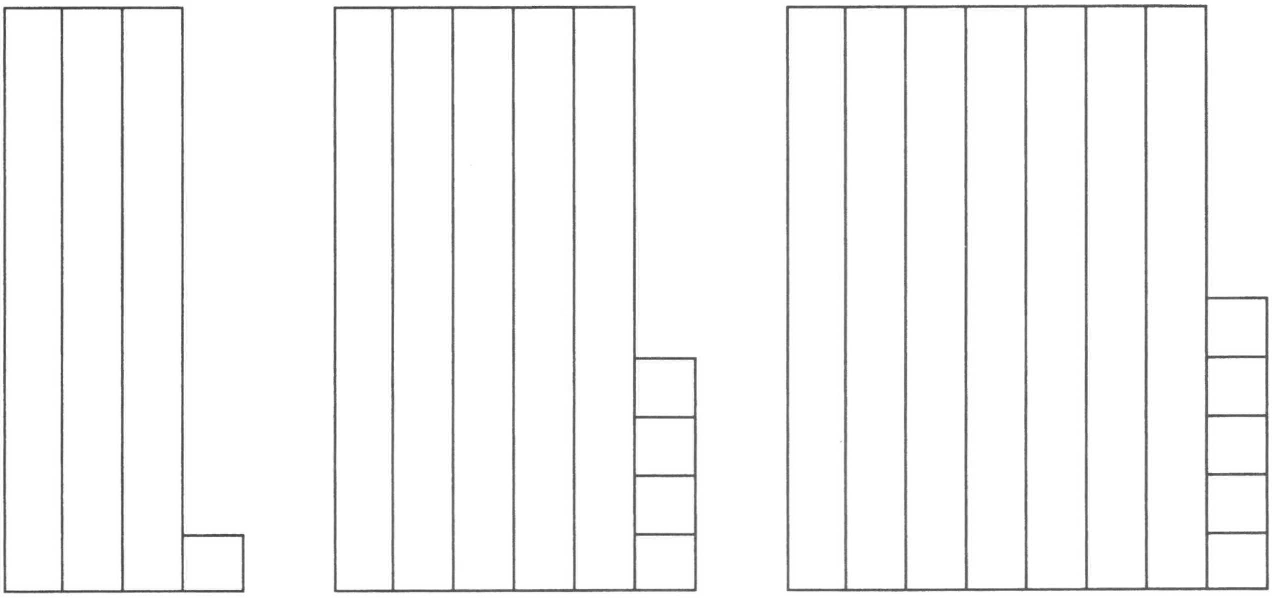

| ☐ tens | ☐ units | ☐ tens | ☐ units | ☐ tens | ☐ units |

→ ☐   → ☐   → ☐

▶ **Ring the groups of ten. Write the number.**

☐ frogs

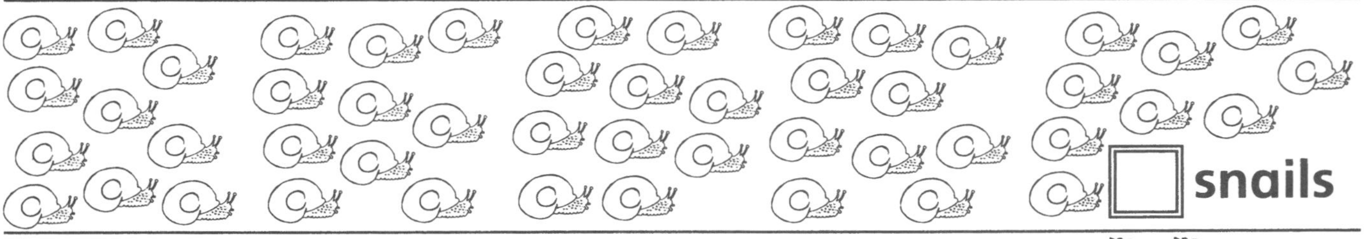

☐ snails

☐ apples

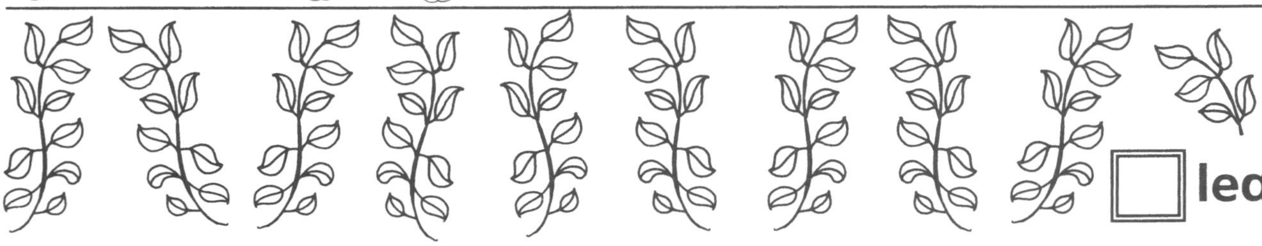

☐ leaves

6

Money

▶ Draw coins to show 50p in each money box.

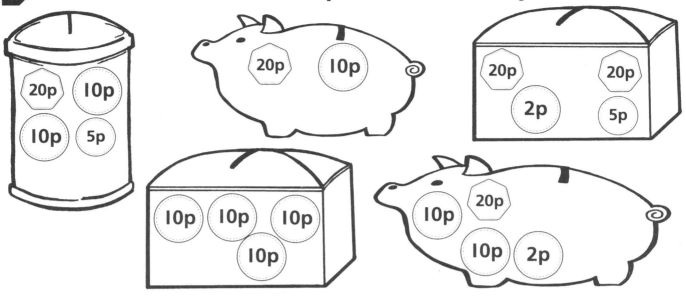

▶ How much money has each child got?
Colour the pile with the most money in it.

Jane ☐ p   Tom ☐ p   Mike ☐ p   Sita ☐ p

Who has least money? ☐

▶ Draw coins to pay for these.

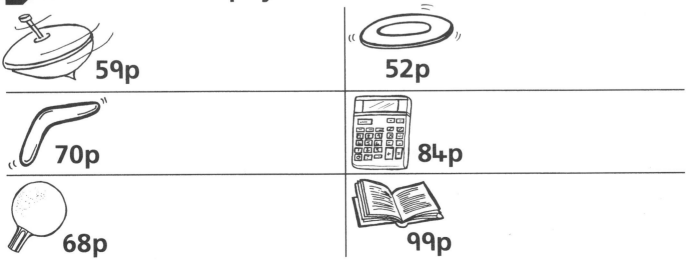

7

Money

▶ Draw the least number of coins needed to make the following amounts.

55p	
69p	
72p	
87p	

48 p	25 p	31 p	40 p

▶ Take 50p to the shop. How much change will you have? Draw the coins.

☐ p   change ☐ p

change ☐ p   ☐ p

☐ p   change ☐ p

change ☐ p   ☐ p

8

Adding and taking

▶ **Add 10.**

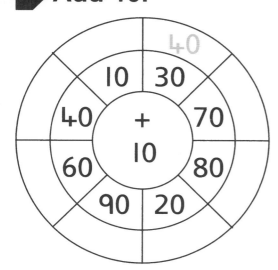
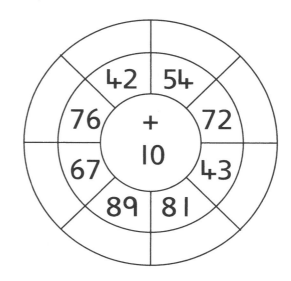

▶ **Count on.**

| 50 51 52 53 54 55 56 57 58 59 60 61 62 63 64 65 66 67 68 69 70 71 72 73 74 75 76 77 78 79 80 |

Count on 10	Count on 9	Count on 11
55 → 65	67 →	61 →
57 →	65 →	69 →
51 →	62 →	68 →
58 →	63 →	64 →

▶ **Count back.**

| 40 41 42 43 44 45 46 47 48 49 50 51 52 53 54 55 56 57 58 59 60 61 62 63 64 65 66 67 68 69 70 |

Count back 10	Count back 10	Count back 11
55 →	64 →	51 →
52 →	69 →	61 →
56 →	68 →	59 →
59 →	62 →	65 →

▶ **Add and take away.**

85 – 10 → ☐   55 + 11 → ☐   68 – 9 → ☐   62 + 9 → ☐

64 – 9 → ☐   48 + 11 → ☐   57 + 11 → ☐   88 – 9 → ☐

9

Solve the problem

► **Follow the jumps. Write the answers in the boxes.**

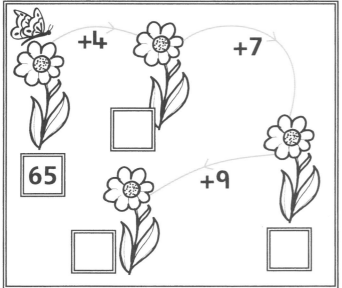

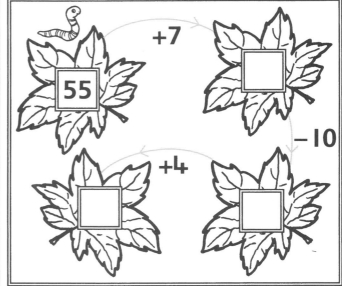

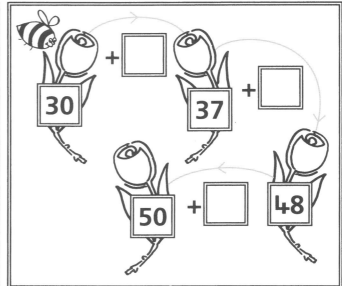

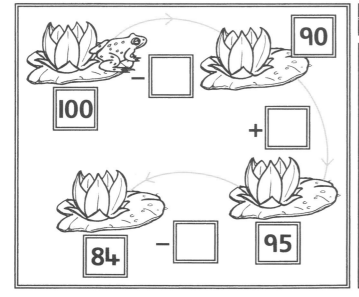

► **Make up your own.**

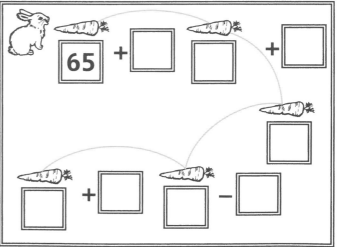

10

Measuring

▶ How many metres long? Estimate first.

	estimate	measure
door		
classroom – long		
P.E. mat		
corridor – long		
hall – long		
piano		
cupboard		
playground – long		
you choose		
you choose		
you choose		

▶ Measure yourself and a friend.
Compare your measurements.

my height _____ m

my friend's height _____ m

my arm span _____ m

my friend's arm span _____ m

my stride _____ m

my friend's stride _____ m

11

Months of the year

| January February March April May June July August September October November December |

▶ **Write the missing months of the year.**

| January   February _____ _____ |

| May   June _____ August _____ |

| _____ November _____ |

▶ **Find out in which month the children in your class were born. Colour a square for the month in which each child was born.**

[   ] children were born in October.

Most children were born in [   ]

10											
9											
8											
7											
6											
5											
4											
3											
2											
1											
Jan.	Feb.	March	April	May	June	July	Aug.	Sept.	Oct.	Nov.	Dec.

Time

Draw the hands on the clocks.
Use red for the hour hand and blue for the minute hand.

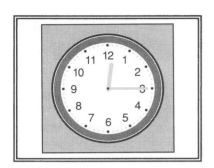

¹/₄ past 12

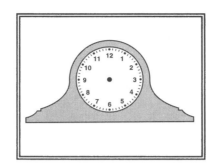

¹/₄ past 7

¹/₄ past 9

¹/₄ past 6

¹/₄ past 11

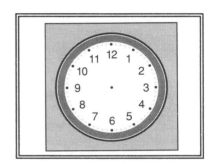

¹/₄ past 4

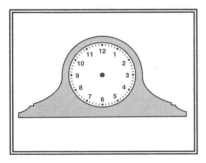

¹/₄ to 8

¹/₄ to 2

¹/₄ to 10

¹/₄ to 5

¹/₄ to 1

¹/₄ to 3

Time

Write the time.

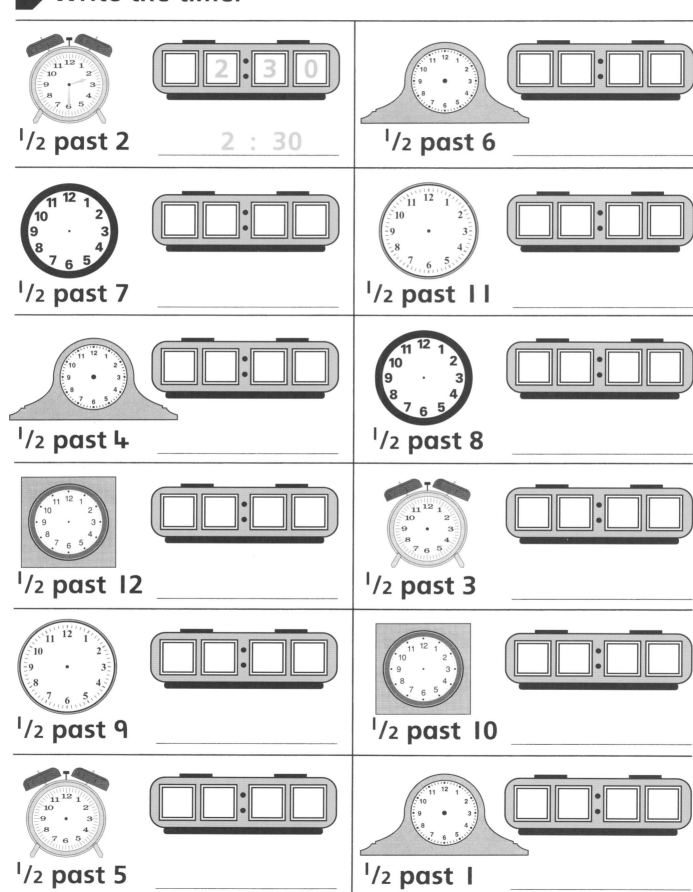

¹/₂ past 2   2 : 30

¹/₂ past 6

¹/₂ past 7

¹/₂ past 11

¹/₂ past 4

¹/₂ past 8

¹/₂ past 12

¹/₂ past 3

¹/₂ past 9

¹/₂ past 10

¹/₂ past 5

¹/₂ past 1

14

Odds and evens

 The postman delivers letters to each even number. Colour the even numbers red.

| 1 | 2 | 3 | 4 | 5 | 6 | 7 | 8 | 9 | 10 | 11 | 12 | 13 | 14 | 15 | 16 | 17 | 18 | 19 | 20 |

The paper girl delivers newspapers to each odd number. Colour the odd numbers green.

| 1 | 2 | 3 | 4 | 5 | 6 | 7 | 8 | 9 | 10 | 11 | 12 | 13 | 14 | 15 | 16 | 17 | 18 | 19 | 20 |

Join the odd numbers with a blue crayon.
Join the even numbers with a yellow crayon.

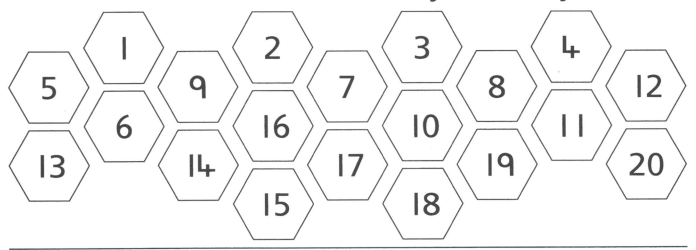

Write the missing numbers, using red for even numbers and green for odd numbers.

21	22							31	
			40						47
	52				58				

Make your own sets of odd and even numbers.

a set of odd numbers

a set of even numbers

15

Numbers

▶ Colour each balloon with the colour of its nearest 10.
Join the balloon to its nearest 10.

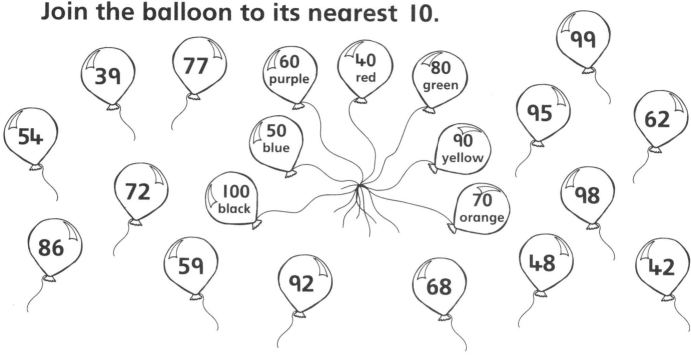

▶ Find 3 numbers which add up to the number in the triangle.

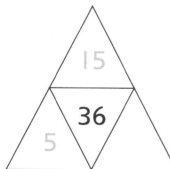

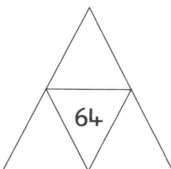

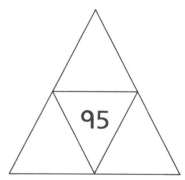

▶ Use these numbers to make up your own sums.

(25)(55)(30) 55 – 25 → 30

(78)(22)(56)

⬡ 38 ⬡ 99 ⬡ 61

Adding and taking

▶ **Use rods to help you**

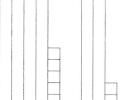

Add

65 + 22 → 87   49 + 20 →   31 + 45 →

72 + 17 →   16 + 7 →   82 + 14 →

55 + 24 →   33 + 66 →   71 + 25 →

Take away

84 − 12 → 72   68 − 23 →   97 − 24 →

56 − 25 →   45 − 15 →   89 − 27 →

49 − 15 →   78 − 54 →   54 − 12 →

▶ **Add**

TU	TU
25	36
+13	+11

TU	TU
28	44
+71	+53

▶ **Take away**

TU	TU
84	78
− 42	− 57

TU	TU
95	84
− 61	− 14

▶ **Take away and add. Look at the sign + or −**

TU	TU	TU	TU
36	42	85	97
− 24	+14	+13	− 63

TU	TU	TU	TU
48	59	65	99
+ 3	− 48	+ 32	− 33

17

Solve the problem

There are 68 bees in this hive. 25 bees buzz away to collect nectar.

TU

68	in the hive.
− 25	buzz away.
43	

▶ How many bees are left in the hive? ☐

There are 2 apple trees in the garden.

One tree has 36 apples on it.

The other tree has 43 apples on it.

TU

☐
+ ☐

▶ How many apples can be picked? ☐

There are 64 fish in the pond.

Tom catches 22 fish and Sam catches 35 fish.

TU

☐
+ ☐

TU

☐
− ☐

▶ How many fish are caught? ☐

▶ How many fish are left in the pond? ☐

Fred planted 96 carrot seeds.

83 seeds grew into carrots.

How many seeds didn't grow?

TU

☐
− ☐

TU

☐
− ☐

Rabbits ate 33 of the carrots.

▶ How many carrots were left? ☐

Money

▶ **Draw arrows to show which sets are worth 50p.**

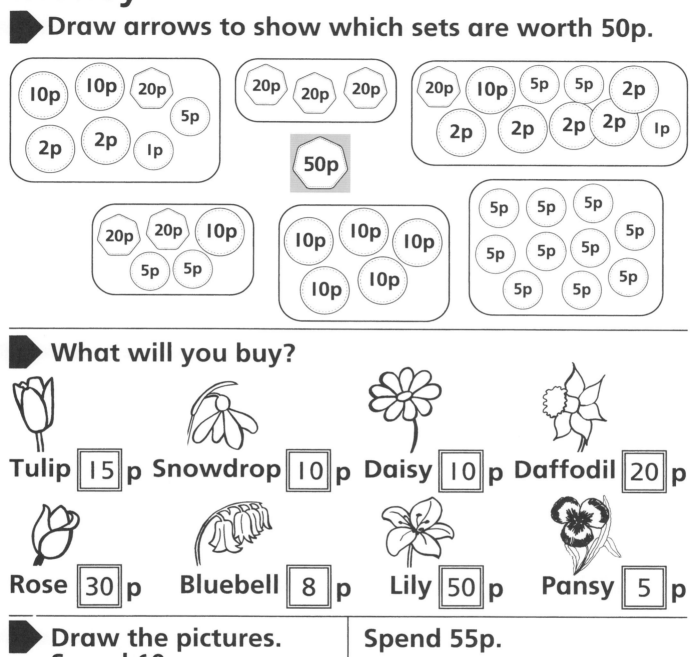

▶ **What will you buy?**

Tulip $\boxed{15}$ p   Snowdrop $\boxed{10}$ p   Daisy $\boxed{10}$ p   Daffodil $\boxed{20}$ p

Rose $\boxed{30}$ p   Bluebell $\boxed{8}$ p   Lily $\boxed{50}$ p   Pansy $\boxed{5}$ p

▶ **Draw the pictures.**
Spend 60p.

Spend 55p.

Spend 90p.

Spend 78p.

Spend 18p.

Spend 25p.

Sale

► Take 30p off anything over 50p.

98 p / 68 p	35 p / ☐ p	47 p / ☐ p	55 p / ☐ p

| 54 p / ☐ p | 63 p ☐ p | 75 p ☐ p | 21 p ☐ p |

► How much will these now cost? Draw the coins.

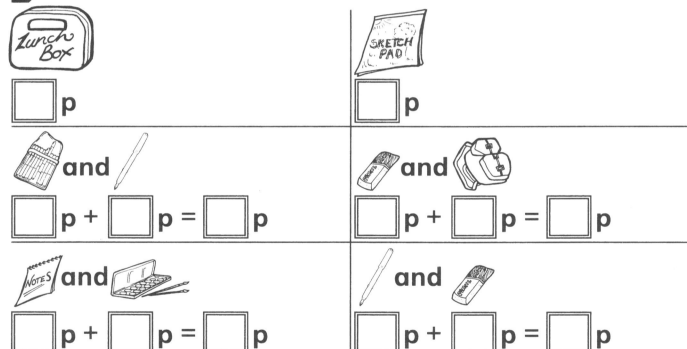

Lunch Box
☐ p

Sketch Pad
☐ p

and
☐ p + ☐ p = ☐ p

and
☐ p + ☐ p = ☐ p

Notes and
☐ p + ☐ p = ☐ p

and
☐ p + ☐ p = ☐ p

► Match to the change from 75p.

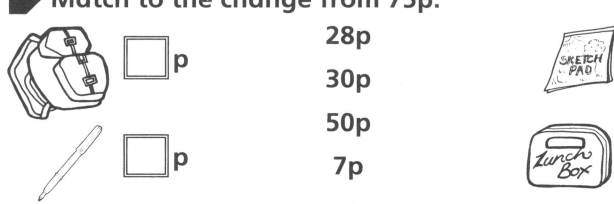

☐ p

☐ p

28p

30p

50p

7p

☐ p

☐ p

Money

▶ **Make £1.00**

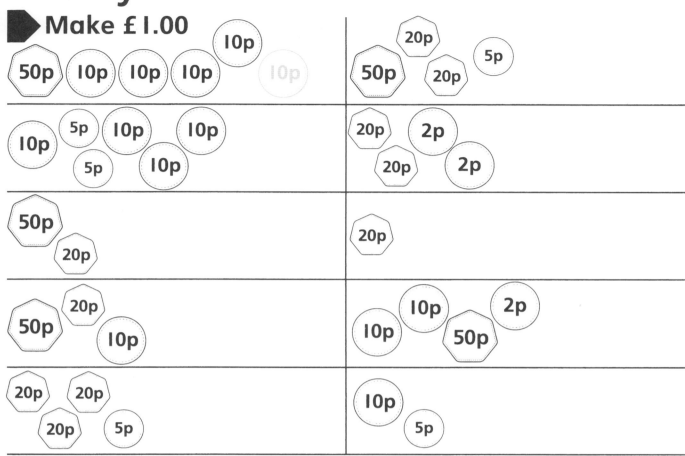

▶ **How much have the children saved?**

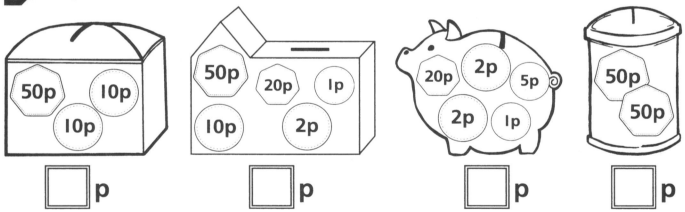

☐ p	☐ p	☐ p	☐ p

Colour the money box with the most money in it.
Draw a red circle round the money box with the least money in it.

These children are going to spend 50p each.
How much change have they left?

 Alex has ☐ p left. Rivi has ☐ p left. Jill has ☐ p left.  Alan has ☐ p left.

Counting in tens

▶ **Count the leaves on each stem.**

10									
leaves	leaves	leaves	leaves	leaves	leaves	leaves	leaves	leaves	leaves

1 stem has	10	leaves
2 stems have		leaves
3 stems have		leaves
4 stems have		leaves
5 stems have		leaves
6 stems have		leaves
7 stems have		leaves
8 stems have		leaves
9 stems have		leaves
10 stems have		leaves

Mr Jones has 8 apple trees in his garden. Each tree has 10 apples on it.

How many apples has Mr Jones got?

☐ apples

▶ **Write numbers in tens.**

10   20

Complete the sums.

2 (10) → 20   5 (10) → ☐   8 (10) → ☐

10 (10) → ☐   7 (10) → ☐   9 (10) → ☐

3 (10) → ☐   6 (10) → ☐   4 (10) → ☐

▶ Can you work these out?

11 (10) → ☐

12 (10) → ☐

Weighing

Weigh out 2kg of plasticine.
Make 2 different models with
your plasticine.
Draw your models here.

**Does it weigh
1kg? ✗ or ✔**

Estimate ▢

Measure ▢

**Does it weigh
1kg? ✗ or ✔**

Estimate ▢

Measure ▢

**Look around the classroom to find objects weighing
about 1kg. Count and draw them.**

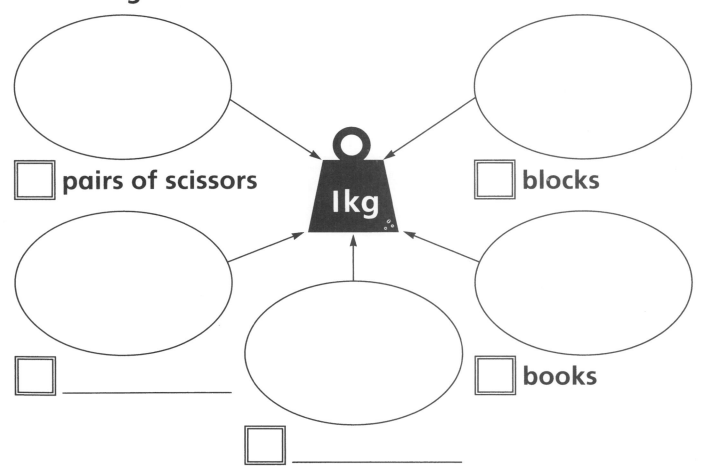

▢ pairs of scissors

▢ blocks

▢ _____

▢ books

▢ _____

Capacity

▶ Use a yoghurt pot and then a mug to fill each container with water.
Write down how many it takes.

To fill	a yoghurt pot		a mug	
	estimate	measure	estimate	measure
margarine tub				
jug				
beaker				
bottle				

▶ Estimate how much the containers will hold.
Tick a box with a blue crayon for your estimate.
Check with a litre container. Tick the correct box with a red crayon.

To fill	less than a litre	more than a litre	about 1 litre
jug			
bottle			
soap container			
squeeze bottle			
bucket			
mug			
teapot			
ice-cream carton			

24

Shape and pattern

▶ **Colour the shapes that have right angles.**

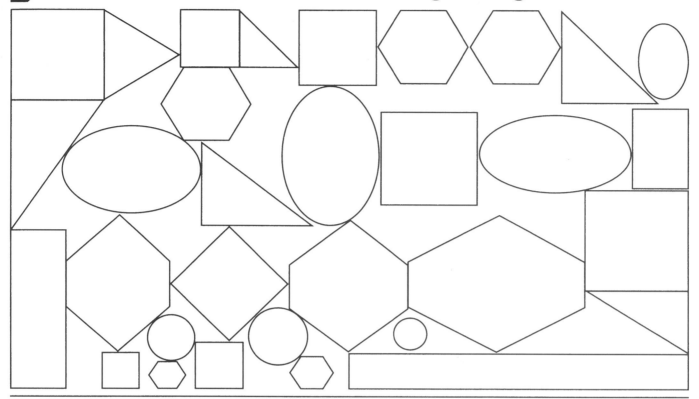

▶ **Draw shapes with the correct number of right angles.**

4 right angles

2 right angles

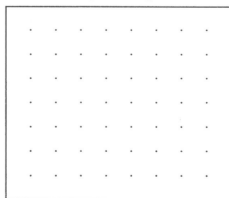

▶ **Draw your own pattern using shapes with right angles.**

Area

▶ **Fold a 5cm square like this.** Cut along the fold.
Fold both triangles in half and cut along the
folds. Use the triangles to find out how many will
fit into these shapes.

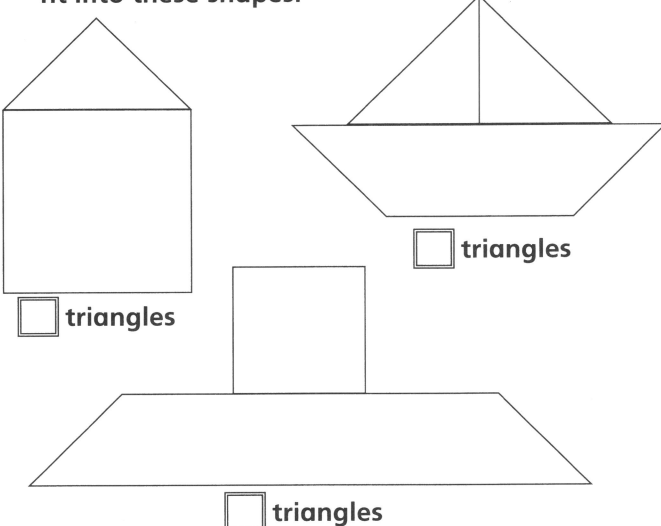

▢ **triangles**

▢ **triangles**

▢ **triangles**

▶ **Make these shapes using your triangles.**

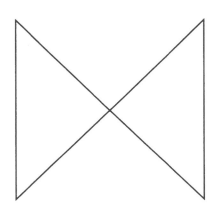

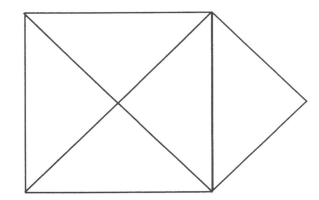

Shape and pattern

► Use the dots to help you draw shapes and make a pattern.

Colour your pattern.

► Colour these triangles to make a picture.

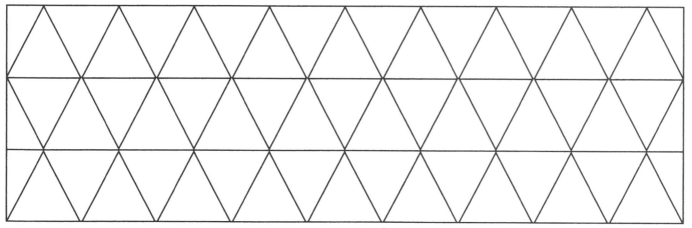

Adding and taking

► **Fill in the missing numbers.**

51	52					57			60
61				65					
							78		
	82								
								99	

► **Add 2 numbers to make the sum.**

 $51 + 22 \rightarrow 73$

$\square + \square \rightarrow 89$

$\square + \square \rightarrow 65$

$\square + \square \rightarrow 94$

$\square + \square \rightarrow 81$

$\square + \square \rightarrow 10$

► **Take a smaller number from a bigger number to make the sum.**

$75 - 15 \rightarrow 60$

$\square - \square \rightarrow 55$

$\square - \square \rightarrow 69$

$\square - \square \rightarrow 72$

$\square - \square \rightarrow 58$

$\square - \square \rightarrow 65$

► **What do you have to do to make the answers correct?**

55   + 10   65   87   99

58   52   74   63

64   69   90   100

28

At the Café

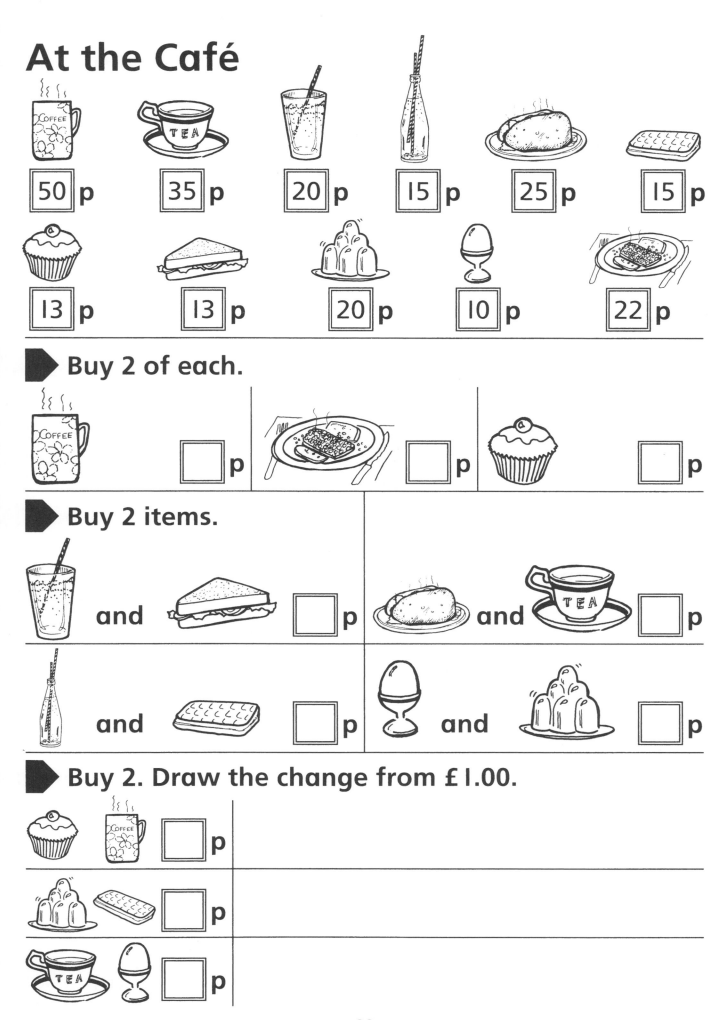

50 p	35 p	20 p	15 p	25 p	15 p
13 p	13 p	20 p	10 p	22 p	

▶ **Buy 2 of each.**

☐ p   ☐ p   ☐ p

▶ **Buy 2 items.**

and ☐ p   and ☐ p

and ☐ p   and ☐ p

▶ **Buy 2. Draw the change from £1.00.**

☐ p

☐ p

☐ p

Number machines

▶ **Start at 50.**

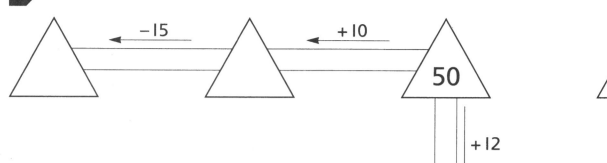

▶ **Start at 68.**

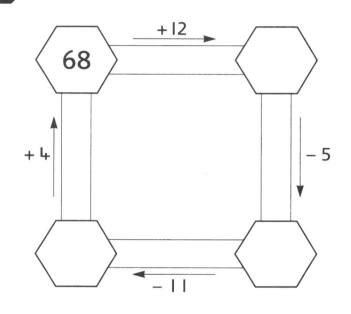

▶ **Find your way out of the castle.**
Start at 54.

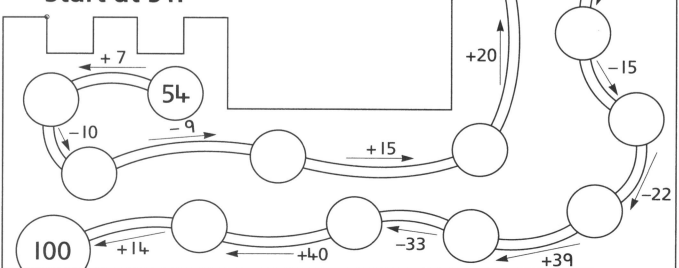